# SAILOR JACK SERIES

SAILOR JACK AND HOMER POTS

SAILOR JACK AND EDDY

SAILOR JACK

SAILOR JACK AND BLUEBELL'S DIVE

SAILOR JACK AND BLUEBELL

SAILOR JACK AND THE JET PLANE

SAILOR JACK AND THE BALL GAME

SAILOR JACK'S NEW FRIEND

SAILOR JACK AND THE TARGET SHIP

SAILOR JACK GOES NORTH

pictures by William Tanis

# SAILOR JACK
# AND
# HOMER POTS

*by Selma and Jack Wassermann*

*Benefic Press*      *Chicago*

Publishing Division of Beckley-Cardy Company
**Atlanta**    **Dallas**    **Long Beach**    **Portland**

# CONTENTS

Copyright 1961 by Benefic Press

All Rights Reserved

Printed in the United States of America

Library of Congress
Number 61-7675

## Homer Pots

This is the SHARK.

The SHARK can dive.

Sailors work on the SHARK.

This is Jack.

He is a sailor.

Homer Pots is a sailor, too.

Captain White is on the SHARK.

He is the SHARK'S captain.

This is Bluebell.

Bluebell is not a sailor.

Jack is at work.

Bluebell likes to look at Jack.

This is Homer at work.
He likes to work.
Homer Pots is a good sailor.

Homer's work looks good.
Homer's work is good.
How the sailors like it!

## No Work for Homer

Bluebell looked at the sailors.

"Dive!" said Captain White.

"Dive!" said a sailor.

"Dive!" said Bluebell.
"Ding! Ding!"

Down went the SHARK!
Down!
Down!
Down!

In the SHARK, the sailors worked.
Sailor Jack worked.
Homer Pots worked, too.

Homer Pots looked at the work.

It looked good.

He did not look down.

# Up went Homer Pots!

# Down came Homer Pots!

"Captain! Captain!" said Homer Pots.

Captain White came.

The sailors came, too.

It did not look good.

The sailors looked.
Captain White looked, too.
They looked at Homer Pots.

"This is not good," said the captain.

The sailors went to work.

They worked on Homer Pots.

"This is not good!" said a sailor.
"You can not work now."

The captain looked at Homer Pots.
He looked at the sailors.
"Who can do this work?" he said.
Not a sailor looked up.

## "Is It Good?"

The captain went to Sailor Jack.
Jack looked up at Captain White.

"It is up to you!" said the captain.
"Homer can not work."
Jack did not like it.
"Up to you!" said Bluebell.
"Aaaaaak! Up to you!"

Jack worked and worked.

The work was not good.

Bluebell did not look at Jack.

How Jack worked!

"Look!" said the sailors.
"This is Jack's work!
Is it good?"

Jack came in.

"Did you like it?" he said.

The sailors did not look up.

"Aaaaaak!" said Bluebell.

## Can Jack Make It?

"Look, captain!" said a sailor.
The captain looked.

"Jack," said the captain.
"Can you make this?"
"I can make it," Jack said.
"Aaaaak!" said Bluebell.

Jack went to work.
Bluebell went to work.
How they worked!

Jack looked at the work.

"Look!" said Jack to Bluebell.

Bluebell looked.

"Aaak!" said Bluebell. "Aaaaaak!"

The sailors looked at Jack's work.

They looked at Jack.
They looked at Bluebell.
They looked and looked.

## Up, Shark! Up!

Jack worked on and on.

"This I can make!" he said.

"Can make!" said Bluebell.

"Ding! Ding!"

Sailor Jack went in.

Bluebell went in, too.

They did not look at the work.

"Captain! Captain!" said a sailor.
"Look! Look at this!"
"Who did it?" said the sailor.

Captain White came in.
"Up!" he said.
"Up, SHARK! Up!"

Up went the SHARK.

Captain White went to work.

The sailors went to work.

How they worked!

They worked and worked.
Jack looked on.
Bluebell looked on.
They did not like it.

## Captain White and the Sailors Work

Captain White looked at the sailors.
"The work is not good," he said.
"Jack can not do Homer's work."
The sailors looked at Captain White.

The sailors went.

The sailors came.

The sailors worked.
The captain looked.
"You can make it!" he said.
On and on they worked.

Captain White looked at the work.

"How good this is!" he said.

"This is it!"

"You are good sailors."

"Look, Homer!" said the captain.
"The sailors did this for you.
Now you can work!"
Homer Pots liked the work.

Jack looked at Homer.

He looked at Captain White.

"Homer can work," Jack said.

"It is good."

"Good! Ding! Ding!" said Bluebell.

## Good Work, Jack!

Homer Pots went to work.

He worked and worked.

The sailors liked the work.

"Dive!" said the captain.

"Dive!" said a sailor.

"Dive!" said Bluebell.
"Ding! Ding!"

Down went the SHARK!
Up went Jack.

"Good work, Jack!" said a sailor.

"Good work!" said Bluebell.

"Good work! Ding! ding."

# VOCABULARY

The total vocabulary of this book is 34 words, excluding proper names. The 25 words in roman type should be familiar to children reading at preprimer level. The 9 words above preprimer level are shown in italic type. The number indicates the page on which the word first appears.

| | | |
|---|---|---|
| a  6 | He  13 | said  10 |
| and  18 | *How*  9 | *sailors*  5 |
| *at*  8 | | |
| | I  27 | the  5 |
| *came*  14 | In  12 | They  16 |
| can  21 | is  5 | This  5 |
| *captain*  6 | it  9 | to  8 |
| | likes  7 | |
| did  13 | look  7 | Up  14 |
| *dive*  5 | | |
| down  11 | *make*  27 | |
| | | went  11 |
| | | *Who*  19 |
| for  42 | No  10 | *work*  7 |
| | not  13 | |
| good  9 | on  17 | You  18 |